Practise Your Phonics w...
Julia Donaldson's
Songbirds

Mr Zed 3

The Ox and the Yak 21

The Doll in the Bin 39

Animal Quiz 57

The Seven Kids 75

Ron Rabbit's Egg 93

OXFORD
UNIVERSITY PRESS

OXFORD
UNIVERSITY PRESS

Great Clarendon Street, Oxford, OX2 6DP, United Kingdom

Oxford University Press is a department of the University of Oxford.
It furthers the University's objective of excellence in research, scholarship
and education by publishing worldwide. Oxford is a registered trade mark
of Oxford University Press in the UK and in certain other countries

Illustrations © Oxford University Press 2009
Text © Julia Donaldson 2009

The moral rights of the author have been asserted

First Edition published 2009
This Edition published 2012

British Library Cataloguing in Publication Data
Data available

978-0-19-279298-3

10 9 8 7 6 5 4

Printed in China

Paper used in the production of this book is a natural, recyclable product
made from wood grown in sustainable forests. The manufacturing process
conforms to the environmental regulations of the country of origin.

Acknowledgements
Series editor Clare Kirtley

Help your child's learning
with essential tips, phonics
support and free eBooks
www.oxfordowl.co.uk

Songbirds

Mr Zed

Story by Julia Donaldson

Pictures by Anni Axworthy

Series editor Clare Kirtley

OXFORD
UNIVERSITY PRESS

Tips for reading Mr Zed together

This book practises these letter patterns:

ll ff zz sh th ng ck
x qu wh

Ask your child to point to these letter patterns and say the sounds (e.g. *wh* as in *which*). Look out for these letter patterns in the story.

Your child might find these words tricky:

he of says she Mr no
gives the to was be

These words are common, but your child may not have learned how to sound them out yet. Say the words for your child if they do not know them.

Before you begin, ask your child read the title by sounding out and blending as much as possible. Look at the picture together. What do you think this story is about?

Remind your child to read unfamiliar words by saying the individual sounds and then blending them together quickly to read the word. When you have finished reading the story, look through it again and:

- Ask your child, *Can you remember what comes out of Mr Zed's hat?* (puppet, mug, quill, pen, ten rabbits)
- Find the words that end with the letter pattern *ck (Patrick, tick, tack, tock)*. Try to write the word *tock*. Say all the sounds in the word (e.g. *t-o-ck*) then write the letter patterns that make each sound.

Patrick is six. He is having fun with Jeff, Ellen and Wong-Jin.

Lots of singing and puffing!

Lots of whizzing! Lots of kicking and yelling!

Then Mum says, "Hush!"
She beckons them in.

"This is Mr Zed," says Mum.

"Sit on the rug!" says Mr Zed.

Mr Zed has a top hat.

"A rabbit is in it!" says Patrick.

Mr Zed taps the hat.
"Tick tack tock!" he says.

"It's a rabbit!" yells Patrick.
But is it?

No, it's a puppet. Mr Zed gives the puppet to Ellen.

Then he taps the hat. "Tick tack tock!"

"It's a rabbit!" yells Jeff.
But is it?

No, it's a mug. Mr Zed gives
it to Jeff.

Then he taps his hat. "Tick tack tock."

"It's a rabbit!" yells Wong-Jin. But is it?

No, it's a quill pen. Mr Zed gives it to Wong-Jin.

"I wish it was a rabbit," says Patrick. "Can I tap the hat?"

Patrick taps the hat and says, "Tick tack tock." Will it be a rabbit?

No, it's ten rabbits!

Songbirds

The Ox and the Yak

Story by Julia Donaldson
Pictures by Thomas Docherty
Series editor Clare Kirtley

OXFORD
UNIVERSITY PRESS

Tips for reading The Ox and the Yak together

This book practises these letter patterns:

ch th ng ck x qu

Ask your child to point to these letter patterns and say the sounds (e.g. *x* as in *fox*). Look out for these letter patterns in the story.

Your child might find these words tricky:

**the of was he said good
one very so some two**

These words are common, but your child may not have learned how to sound them out yet. Say the words for your child if they do not know them.

Before you begin, ask your child read the title by sounding out and blending as much as possible. Look at the picture together. What do you think this story is about?

Remind your child to read unfamiliar words by saying the individual sounds and then blending them together quickly to read the word. When you have finished reading the story, look through it again and:

- Talk about what's in the man's box. Ask your child, *Does it contain good luck? Why?*
- Find the words that rhyme on pages 36-37 (*quack, back*). Try to write the word *quack*. Say all the sounds in the word (e.g. *qu-a-ck*) then write the letter patterns that make each sound.

On the back of an ox
sat a man with a box

and in the man's box
was a bag of odd socks.

On the back of a yak
sat a man with a pack
and in the man's pack
was a duck with a quack.

The man on the ox
met the man with the duck
and he said, "In this box
is a bag of good luck."

The men had a chat
and the duck got a hat.

It was one of the socks
from the bag in the box.

Then the man on the ox
sang a very long song
and the man on the yak
hit a very big gong.

The yak did a jig
and so did the ox
and the duck had some fun
with the bag of odd socks.

35

Then the duck said,
"Quack quack!"
and the two men went back

on the back of the ox
and the back of the yak.

Songbirds

The Doll in the Bin

Story by Julia Donaldson

Pictures by Joelle Dreidemy

Series editor Clare Kirtley

OXFORD
UNIVERSITY PRESS

Tips for reading Doll in the Bin together

This book practises these letter patterns:

ll   ss   ff   sh   th   wh   ng   ck   x

Ask your child to point to these letter patterns and say the sounds (e.g. *ff* as in *cuff*). Look out for these letter patterns in the story.

Your child might find these words tricky:

he   her   the   to   of   she   are   have
come   says   school   gives   wash   let's

These words are common, but your child may not have learned how to sound them out yet. Say the words for your child if they do not know them.

Before you begin, ask your child read the title by sounding out and blending as much as possible. Look at the picture together. What do you think this story is about?

Remind your child to read unfamiliar words by saying the individual sounds and then blending them together quickly to read the word. When you have finished reading the story, look through it again and:

- Ask your child, *Have you ever lost something? How did you feel?*
- Find the words that end with the letter pattern *th* (*Beth*, *with*). Try to write the word *with*. Say all the sounds in the word (e.g. *w-i-th*) then write the letter patterns that make each sound.

This is Beth and this is Jill.
Jill is Beth's doll.

This is Puff. Puff is Beth's cat.
When Beth is in bed,
Puff gets Jill.

Puff is patting Jill.
He pats her into the bin!

The bin men have come to get the rubbish.

The men tip the bins into
the back of a big van.
Jill is in this bin bag!

Beth is sad.

She is missing Jill.

The bin men tip the rubbish into a big pit.

Lots of things are in the pit.
Pots, tubs, boxes . . . and Jill!

This is Tess. Tess is at the rubbish tip with her mum.

"Mum!" says Tess. "Is that a doll in the pit?"

A man picks up the doll.
He gives her to Mum.

Tess is in school. "This doll fell in a pit," she says.

"That's Jill!" says Beth.

Tess gives Jill back to Beth.

Beth gives Tess a set of peg dolls.

Songbirds

Animal Quiz

Story by Julia Donaldson

Pictures by Carol Liddiment

Series editor Clare Kirtley

OXFORD
UNIVERSITY PRESS

Tips for reading Animal Quiz together

This book practises these letter patterns:

ll zz sh ch th ff wh ng
ck x qu

Ask your child to point to these letter patterns and say the sounds (e.g. *zz* as in *buzz*). Look out for these letter patterns in the story.

Your child might find these words tricky:

the of have she she's their or
they do give to into

These words are common, but your child may not have learned how to sound them out yet. Say the words for your child if they do not know them.

Before you begin, ask your child read the title by sounding out and blending as much as possible. Look at the picture together. What do you think this story is about?

Remind your child to read unfamiliar words by saying the individual sounds and then blending them together quickly to read the word. When you have finished reading the story, look through it again and:

- Talk about the animal homes shown on pages 63-66 (a nest and a den). Ask your child, *Which animals live in these homes?*

- Find the words that contain the letter patterns *wh* and *ch* (*which*, *chips*, *chicks*). Try to write the word *which*. Say all the sounds in the word (e.g. *wh-i-ch*) then write the letter patterns that make each sound.

This is the tip of a wing.
Is it a robin, a duck or a bat?

Which animal's leg is this?
Is it an ox, a camel or a rat?

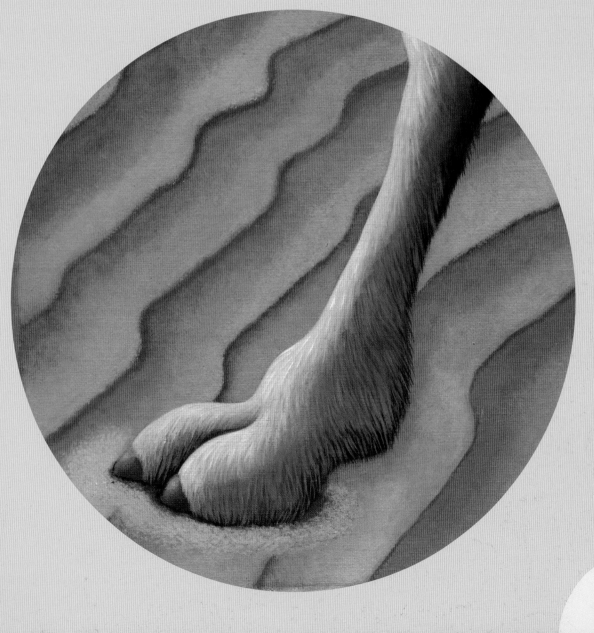

It's a camel! Camels have long legs.

The chicks have a mum.
Is she a gull, a hen or a puffin?

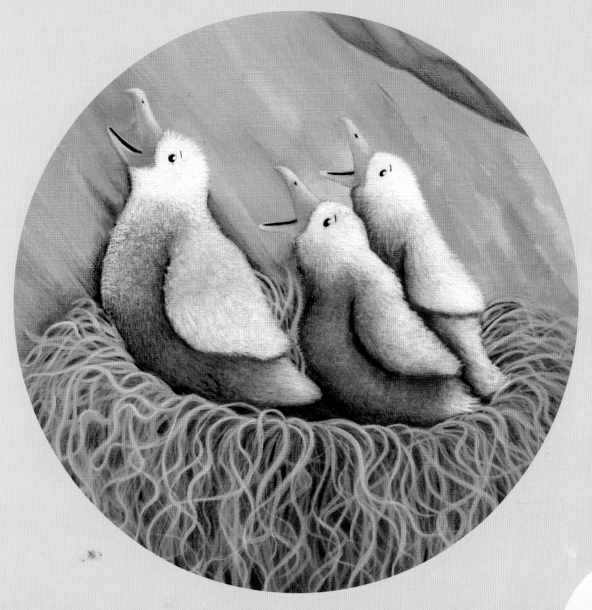

Yes, she's a gull.

Fox cubs in a den. Is their mum a yak, an ox or a vixen?

Yes! Their mum is a vixen.

This is a robin. Will it quack, sing or buzz?

Robins sing. They do not quack or buzz.

This animal is in its mum's pocket.
Is it a cat, a wombat or a bat?

It's a wombat.

Which dish will Mick give to his rabbit? A dish of carrots, jam or chips?

Carrots – not chips or jam!

Seven eggs. Will they hatch into chickens, ducklings or parrots?

Tap, tap, tap! Seven ducklings!

Songbirds

The Seven Kids

Story by Julia Donaldson

Pictures by Andy Hammond

Series editor Clare Kirtley

OXFORD
UNIVERSITY PRESS

Tips for reading The Seven Kids together

This book practises these letter patterns:

ll ff sh th ck x qu

Ask your child to point to these letter patterns and say the sounds (e.g. *sh* as in *shut*). Look out for these letter patterns in the story.

Your child might find these words tricky:

live the do me we no
puts what

These words are common, but your child may not have learned how to sound them out yet. Say the words for your child if they do not know them.

Before you begin, ask your child read the title by sounding out and blending. Look at the picture together. What do you think this story is about?

Remind your child to read unfamiliar words by saying the individual sounds and then blending them together quickly to read the word. When you have finished reading the story, look through it again and:

- Talk about how the fox feels at the end of the story.
- Find the words that begin with the letter pattern *sh* (*shack, shop, shall*). Think of some words that end with the letter pattern *sh* (*fish, dish, wish*). Make up a rhyme using your words (e.g. *a fish on a dish as you wish*).

Seven kids live in a shack
with Mum.

Mum tells the kids, "Do not let the fox in."

Mum is at the shop.

81

83

But it is not Mum. It is the fox,
with a big sack.

The fox puts six kids in his sack.
But Ken kid is in a box.

The fox sets off with his sack.
Ken kid runs.

The fox has a nap. Ken runs
to the shop.

Mum and Ken cut the sack.

The six kids run back to
the shack.

Mum and Ken put six rocks in the sack.

The fox is in his den.

But what is this?

Songbirds

Ron Rabbit's Egg

Story by Julia Donaldson

Pictures by Jonathan Allen

Series editor Clare Kirtley

OXFORD
UNIVERSITY PRESS

Tips for reading Ron Rabbit's Egg together

This book practises these letter patterns:

**ll zz sh ch tch th wh
ng ck x**

Ask your child to point to these letter patterns and say the sounds (e.g. *tch* as in *hatch*). Look out for these letter patterns in the story.

Your child might find these words tricky:

**out of he says give me I
the make have play be**

These words are common, but your child may not have learned how to sound them out yet. Say the words for your child if they do not know them.

Before you begin, ask your child read the title by sounding out and blending as much as possible. Look at the picture together. What do you think this story is about?

Remind your child to read unfamiliar words by saying the individual sounds and then blending them together quickly to read the word. When you have finished reading the story, look through it again and:

- Ask your child, *What would you do with the egg?*
- Find some words that end with the *ch* sound (*hatch, catch, rich, such*). Notice the sound *ch* is spelled two different ways. Try to write the word *catch*. Say all the sounds in the word (e.g. *c-a-tch*) then write the letter patterns that make each sound.

Ron Rabbit has an egg.
"A chicken will hatch out of
this egg," he says.

"Then, when that chicken is a hen, it will give me lots of eggs.

If I sell the eggs, I can get a big pot.

Then I can make lots of jam.

If I sell the jam, I can get a fishing rod.

I will catch lots of fish and sell them.

Then I will be rich! I can have lots of things.

I can have a hammock and
a big box of chocs.

I can have a chess set.

I can have a tennis racket.

I can play jazz on a sax.

I can have a jacket with lots of
pockets and zips and buttons,

and thick mittens, and a hat
with a pompom.

I will be in the jet set!"

But then ... bang!

"That egg had such a thin shell!"
says Ron Rabbit.